MEGA colouring

Parragon

Bath • New York • Singapore • Hong Kong • Cologne • Delhi
Melbourne • Amsterdam • Johannesburg • Shenzhen

This edition published by Parragon Books Ltd in 2014

Parragon
Chartist House
15–17 Trim Street
Bath BA1 1HA, UK
www.parragon.com

ISBN 978-1-4723-4456-4

Printed in China

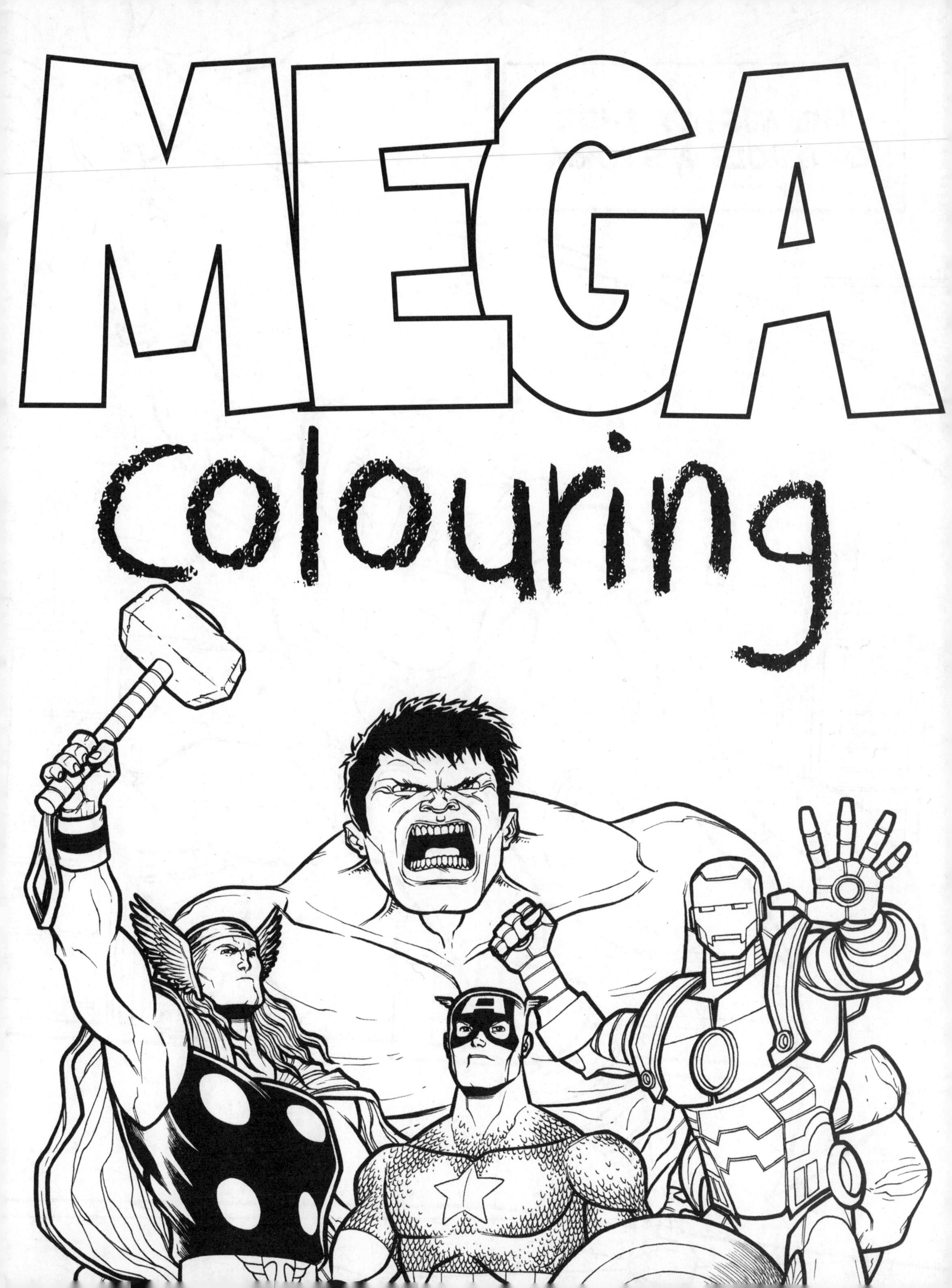
MEGA
Colouring

THE MIGHTY THOR
CONTROLS A STORM.

HULK SMASH! THE HULK RELEASES HIS RAGE.

IRON MAN SOARS
OVER THE CITY.

THE AVENGERS ASSEMBLE!

THOR BANISHES LOKI TO THE
ISLAND OF THE TROLLS.

LOKI SENDS A TROLL TO
EARTH TO CAUSE CHAOS!

CAPTAIN AMERICA
TO THE RESCUE!

THOR LEADS HIS TEAMMATES TO ASGARD.

BRIDGE SMASHED
HELP!
WASP AND ANT-MAN FLY INTO ACTION!

THE INVINCIBLE INVENTOR,
TONY STARK.

THE X-MEN TRAIN IN THE DANGER ROOM.

THE AMAZING SPIDER-MAN
SWINGS THROUGH THE CITY.

THE MIGHTY THOR LEAVES ASGARD TO PROTECT EARTH.

ATTACK OF
THE TROLLS!

CAPTAIN AMERICA'S
SUPER-SOLDIER SERUM STRENGTH.

THE EVIL ELECTRO STRIKES!

WOLVERINE'S CLAWS CAN RIP
THROUGH ANYTHING!

BRUCE BANNER TRANSFORMS
INTO THE INCREDIBLE HULK!

ANT-MAN PACKS
A BIG PUNCH!

ANT-MAN AND WASP
HELP TO DEFEAT LOKI.

ELECTRO USES HIS POWER TO ZAP OUT THE LIGHTS!
TOYZ

CYCLOPS DETECTS DANGER.

EARTH IS UNDER
THOR'S PROTECTION!

THOR'S FATHER, ODIN, IS THE RULER OF ASGARD.

IRON MAN'S REPULSOR RAYS
BLAST THROUGH STEEL!

ICEMAN IS CAUGHT BY SURPRISE.

LOKI WANTS TO
RULE ASGARD.

ELECTRO TRIES TO OUTRUN THE WEB-SLINGER.
TOY

AN ELECTRIFYING BATTLE
ON THE BIG WHEEL.

AVENGERS
ASSEMBLE

ANGEL IS LOCKED IN THE DANGER ROOM!

NOTHING STANDS A CHANCE
AGAINST COLOSSUS!

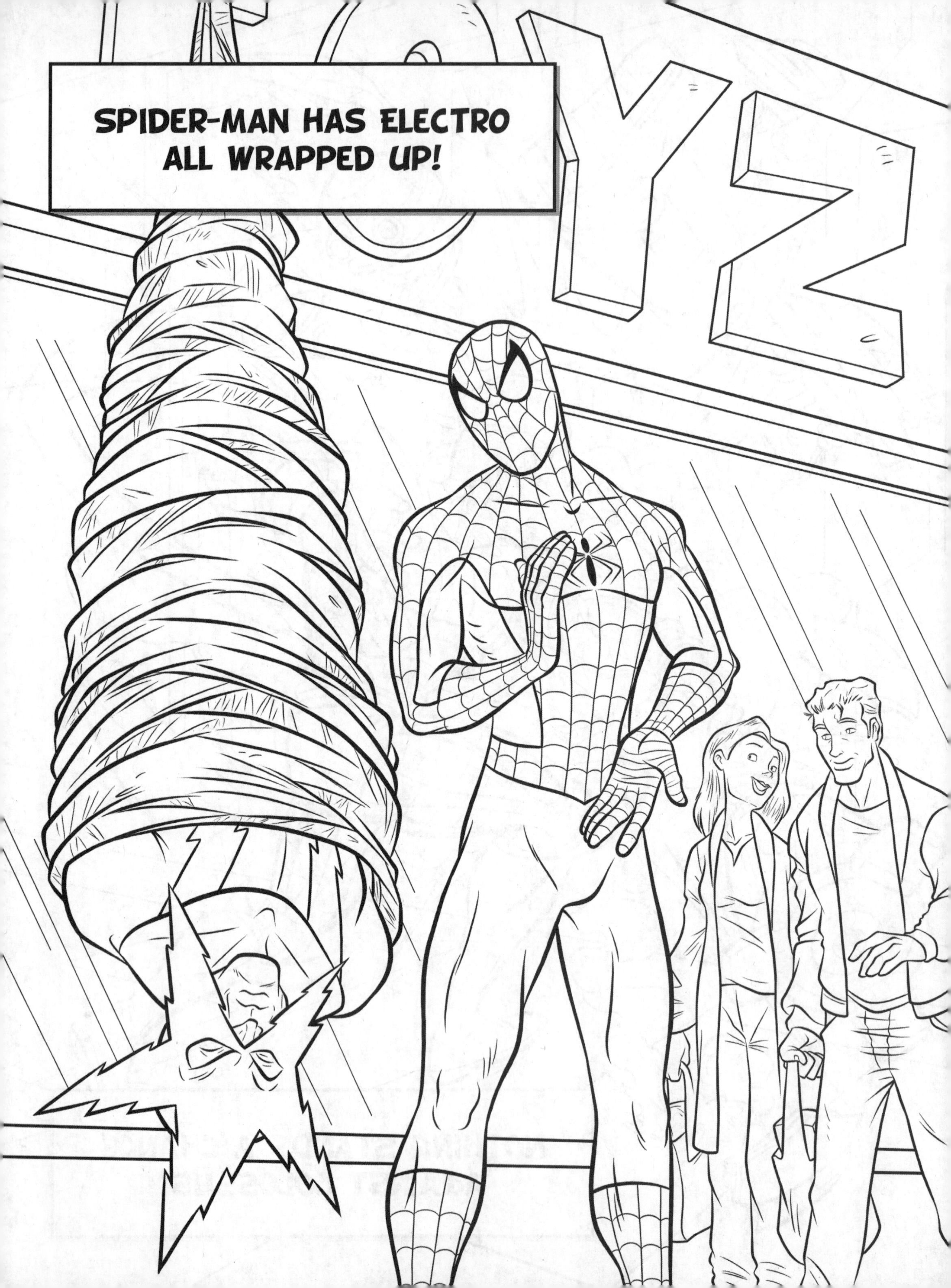
SPIDER-MAN HAS ELECTRO
ALL WRAPPED UP!
YZ

A STORM GIANT THREATENS EARTH!

IRON MAN TAKES THE EVIL
CONTROLLER BY SURPRISE!

DAILY BUGLE
SPIDEY WEB-SHOOTS HIS WAY BACK TO THE DAILY BUGLE.

WOLVERINE STOPS THE EVIL ARCADE TAKING CONTROL.
0:02

THE AVENGERS BATTLE
THE CRIMEBOTS.

FROM SUPER HERO TO SUPER PHOTOGRAPHER.

CAPTAIN AMERICA
IS ON A MISSION.

IRON MAN STRIKES A
VICIOUS ENEMY!

IT'S GAME OVER
FOR ARCADE!

SPIDER-MAN TAKES ON
THE LETHAL LIZARD.

THOR'S HAMMER, MJOLNIR,
HAS HUGE POWER.

THE X-MEN UNITE!

WATCH OUT FOR THE
SUPER-STRONG SANDMAN!

SPIDEY CHASES THE GRUESOME GREEN GOBLIN.

IT'S LIGHTS OUT FOR THE CONTROLLER!

ANGEL ATTACKS THE DANGEROUS BLOB.

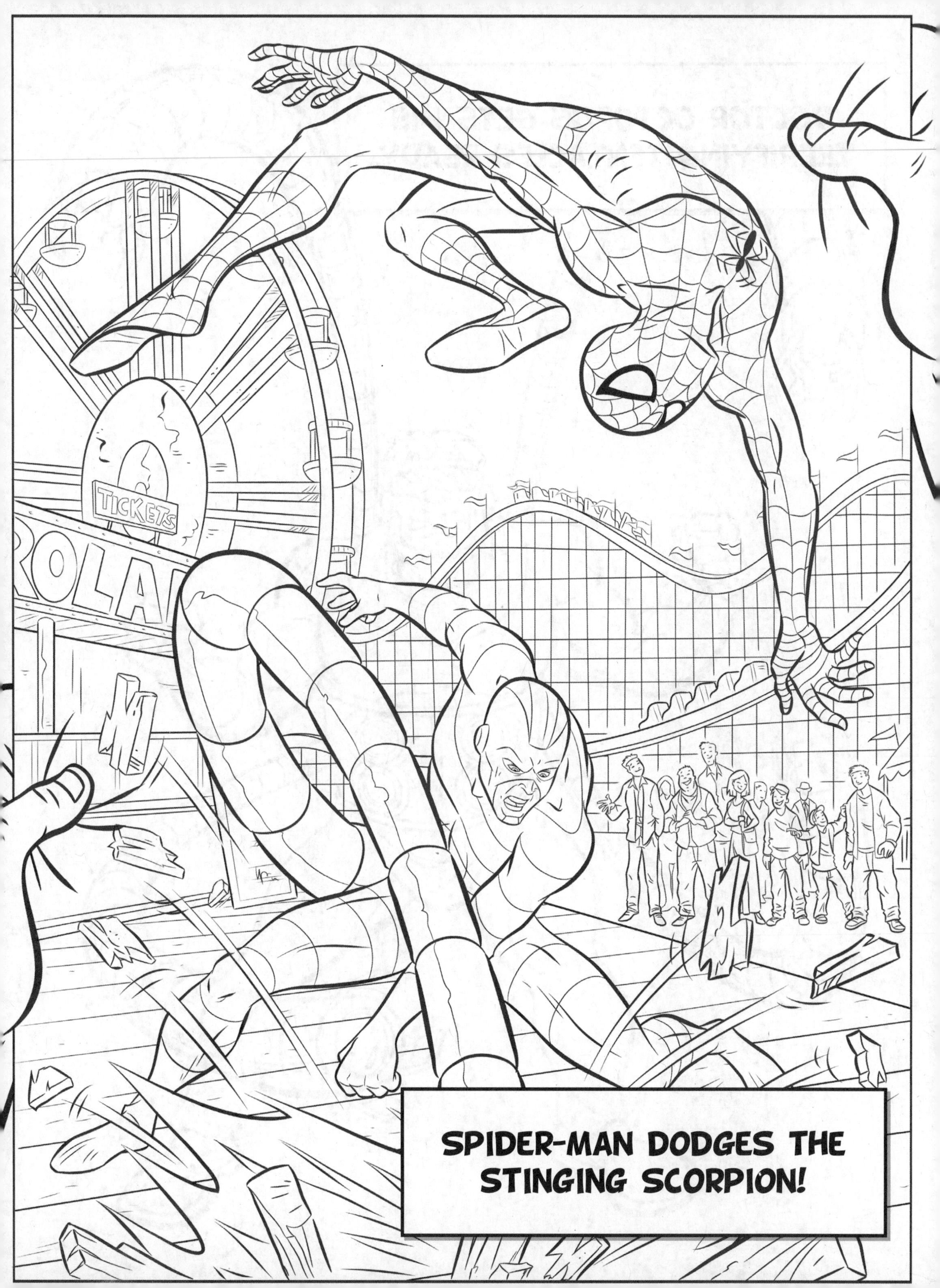
TICKETS
SPIDER-MAN DODGES THE STINGING SCORPION!

DOCTOR OCTOPUS GETS HIS TERRIFYING TENTACLES READY.

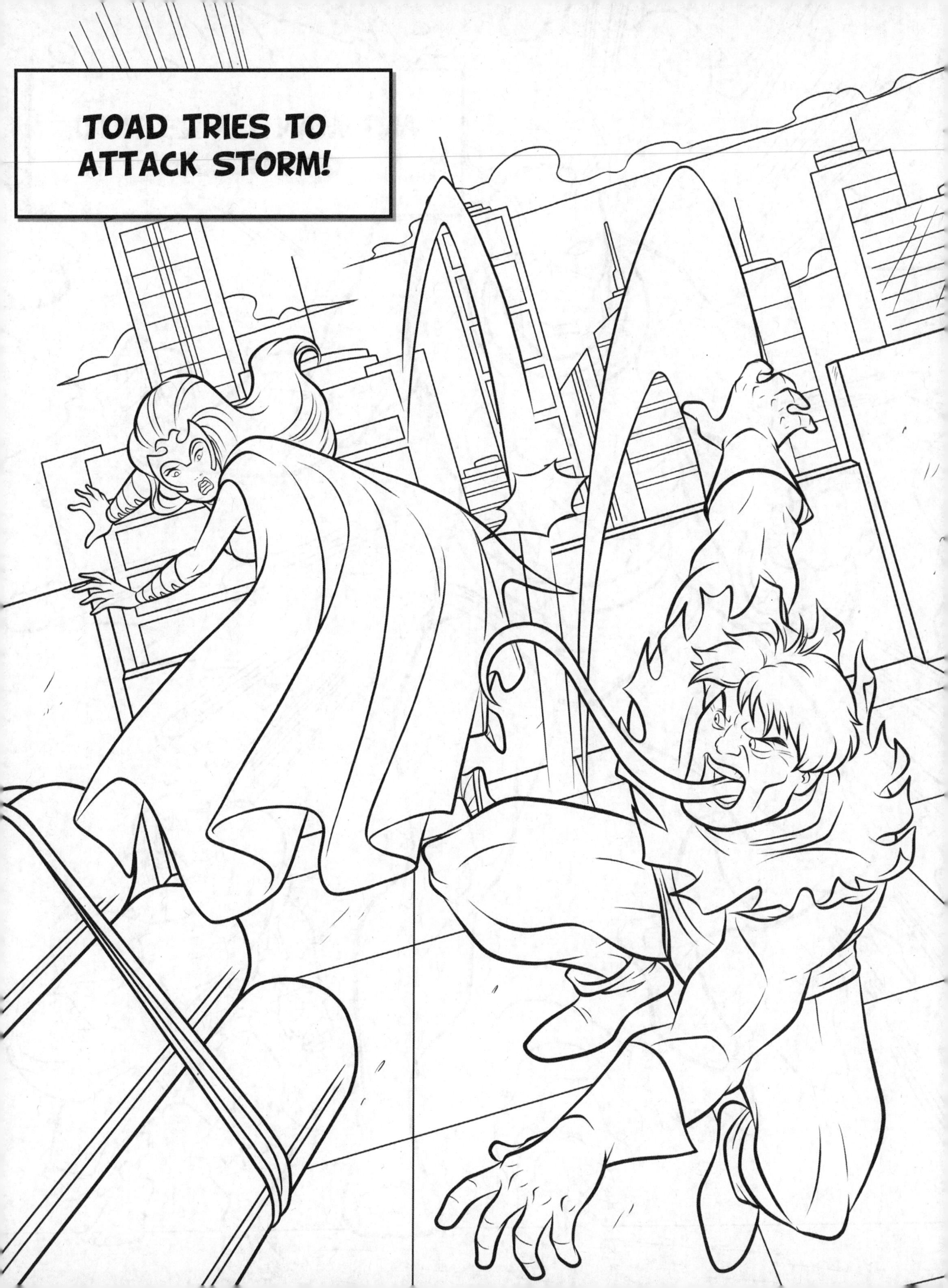
TOAD TRIES TO
ATTACK STORM!

ANT-MAN TURNS INTO GIANT MAN!

THE STORM GIANT PROVES HIS
STRENGTH AGAINST THOR.

BUGLE
ON THE HUNT FOR A SUPER VILLAIN.

THE MENACING MYSTERIO IS
A MASTER OF ILLUSION.

HULK SMASHES A CROWD OF CRIMEBOTS.

SPIDER-MAN'S SPIDER-SENSE
IS TINGLING!

HAVOK JOINS IN THE
FIGHT AGAINST TOAD.

CAPTAIN AMERICA STRIKES
THE ALPHA-BOT!

ICEMAN, WOLVERINE AND BANSHEE LEAP INTO ACTION!

NOTHING CAN STOP
THE JUGGERNAUT!

IRON MAN SOARS TO
THE RESCUE!

THOR BLASTS THE STORM GIANT
WITH A LIGHTNING STRIKE.

SPIDEY DETECTS DANGER ...
IT'S HYDRO-MAN!

THE VILLAINOUS VULTURE
SWOOPS OVER THE CITY.

CAPTAIN AMERICA HURLS
HIS MIGHTY SHIELD.

THE TITANIUM MAN IS
ON THE RAMPAGE!

THOR BATTLES A FIRE GIANT.

SPIDEY GETS CAUGHT IN
HYDRO-MAN'S WAVE.

WOLVERINE'S CLAWS STRIKE
DOWN JUGGERNAUT.

HAMMER HANDS! SANDMAN IS READY TO CAUSE DAMAGE.

POLICE
HULK TAKES OUT THE TRASH!

IRON MAN SHOWS OFF HIS
INDESTRUCTIBLE ARMOUR.

SPIDER-MAN STRIKES THE WATERY MENACE!

THE PRINCE OF ASGARD LEAPS INTO ACTION!

A BATTLE OF STRENGTH.

THE TITANIUM MAN IS TRAPPED
IN HIS OWN ARMOUR!

STORM CONTROLS THE WEATHER
TO DEFEAT SABRETOOTH.

A LIGHTNING STRIKE TAKES DOWN SABRETOOTH.

THOR RESCUES HIS FRIENDS,
THE WARRIORS THREE.

THE WARRIORS THREE
JOIN THE BATTLE!

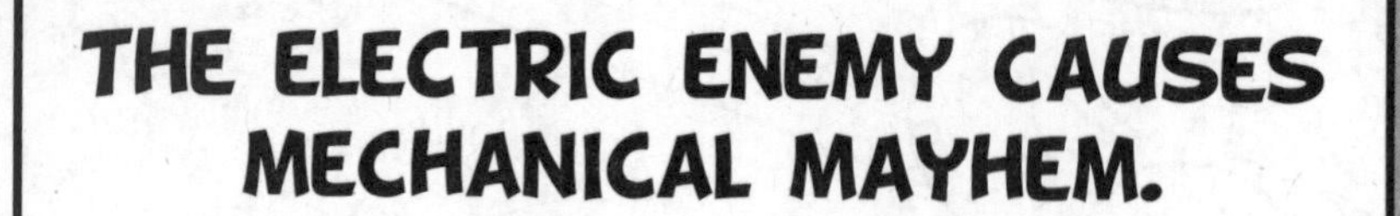
THE ELECTRIC ENEMY CAUSES
MECHANICAL MAYHEM.

IRON MAN ARMOUR:
ACTIVATE!

THE EVIL SHAPE-SHIFTING
MUTANT, MYSTIQUE.

BLACK CAT IS READY TO
TAKE ON SPIDER-MAN.

SKURGE IS A
DANGEROUS ENEMY.

THE WEB-SHOOTER DODGES
A LIGHTNING STRIKE.

AN ON-TARGET
REPULSOR RAY!

MARVEL GIRL LOCATES
MYSTIQUE WITH HER MIND!

TIME TO DEFEAT
TWO VILLAINS!

A FRIEND OF LOKI'S, THE
EVIL ENCHANTRESS.

IRON MAN DEFEATS THE
DANGEROUS SPYMASTER.